D0188428

LLYFRGELLOEDD ABERTAWE
SWANSEA LIBRARIES

8500043263

IMAGINE THAT™

Licensed exclusively to Imagine That Publishing Ltd
Tide Mill Way, Woodbridge, Suffolk, IP12 1AP, UK
www.imaginethat.com
Copyright © 2020 Imagine That Group Ltd
All rights reserved
4 6 8 9 7 5 3
Manufactured in China

Written by Bodhi Hunter
Illustrated by Louise Ellis

All rights reserved. No part of this publication may be reproduced, stored in a retrieval system, or
transmitted in any form or by any means, electronic, mechanical, photocopying, recording or otherwise,
without the prior written permission of the publisher. Neither this book nor any part or any of the
illustrations, photographs or reproductions contained in it shall be sold or disposed of otherwise than as
a complete book, and any unauthorised sale of such part illustration, photograph or reproduction shall be
deemed to be a breach of the publisher's copyright.

ISBN 978-1-78958-480-6

A catalogue record for this book is available from the British Library

LLYFRGELLOEDD ABERTAWE SWANSEA LIBRARIES	
8500043263	
PETERS	6.99
SWSK	

Dream Big!

Written by Bodhi Hunter
Illustrated by Louise Ellis

You can do *anything* – put your mind to it,

Dream BIG – *believe* that you can do it!

You could be a pilot of a plane,

or learn to drive a high-speed train.

You could be a doctor or a teacher,

or find an undiscovered creature.

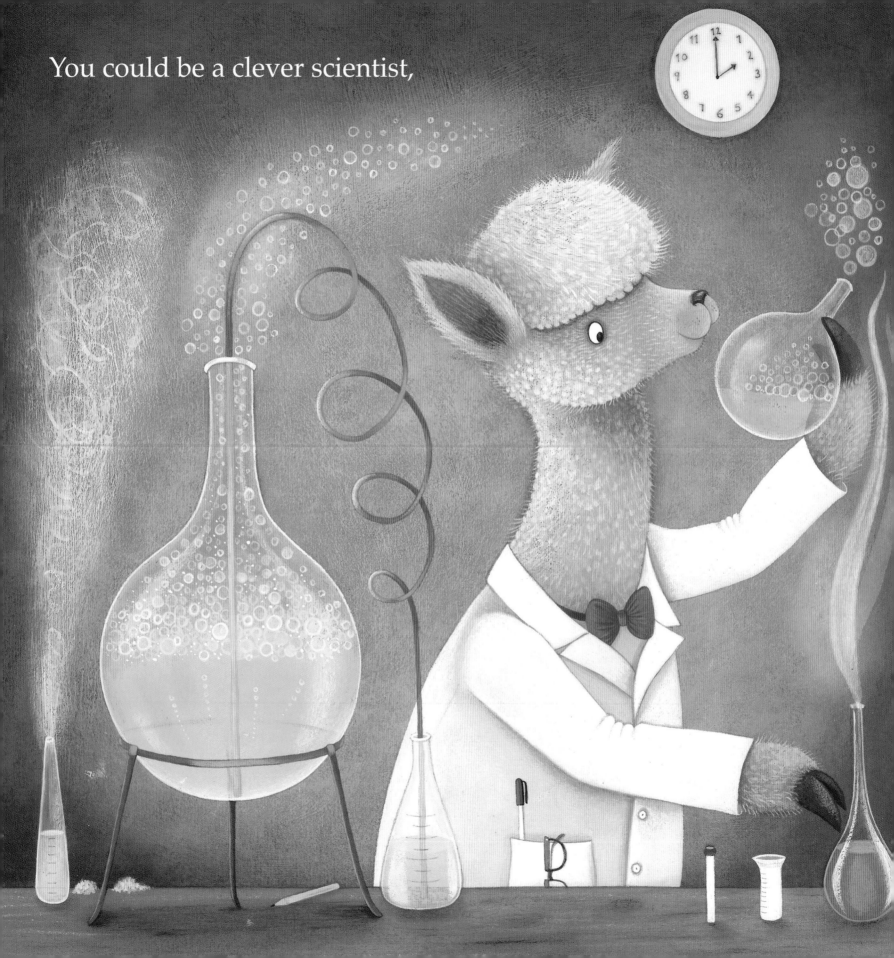

You could be a clever scientist,

or a famous
concert pianist.

You could explore the
ocean deep,

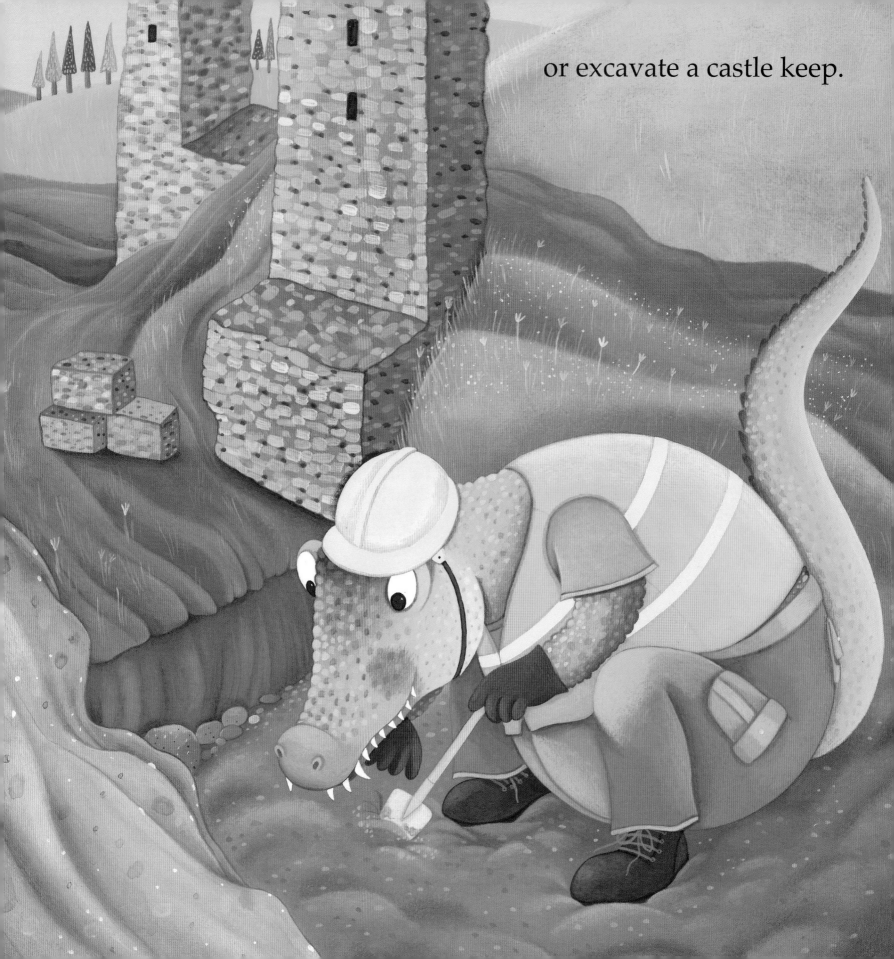

or excavate a castle keep.

You could be
an engineer,

or join the police as your career.

You could work on a construction site,

or be a hero and firefight.

You could act in movies and on TV,

or dance on stage for all to see.

You could play music
in a band,

or drive freight across the land.

You could study law and do good deeds,

or write great books for
kids to read.

You could fly up into outer space,

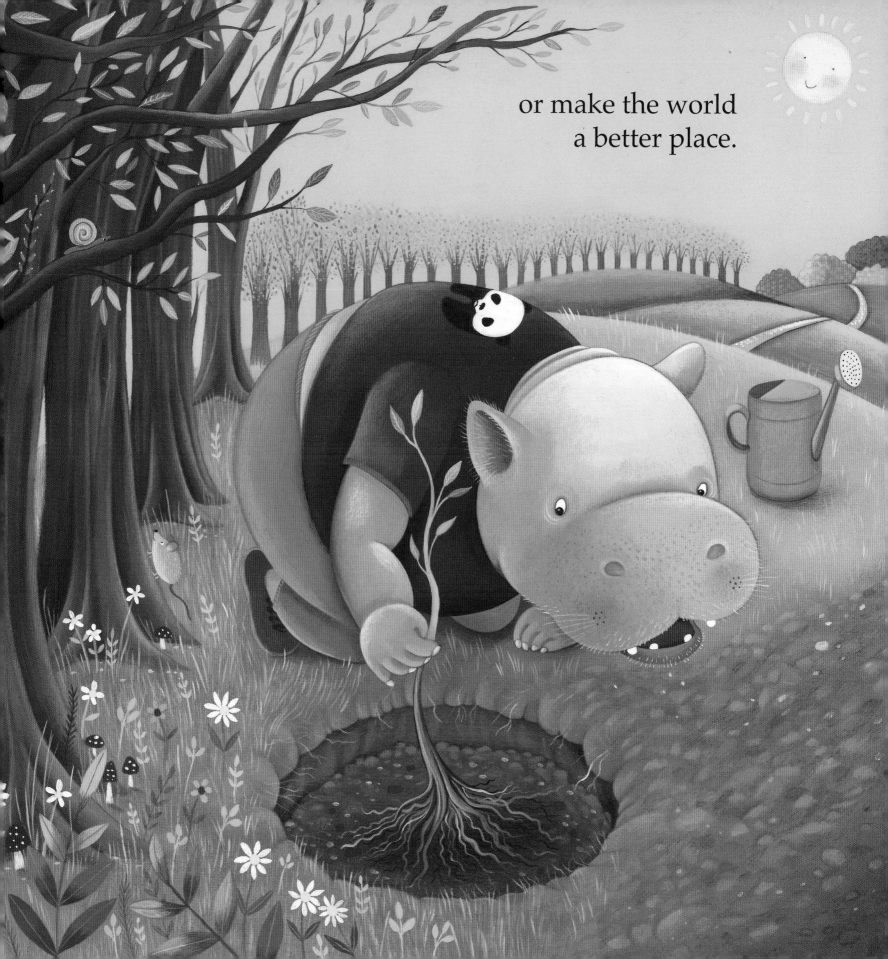

or make the world
a better place.

You can do *anything* – put your mind to it,

Dream BIG – believe that you can do it!